Other titles in this series:
The World's Greatest Business Cartoons
The World's Greatest Cat Cartoons
The World's Greatest Computer Cartoons
The World's Greatest Dad Cartoons
The World's Greatest Do-It-Yourself Cartoons
The World's Greatest Keep-Fit Cartoons
The World's Greatest Golf Cartoons
The World's Greatest Marriage Cartoons
The World's Greatest Middle Age Cartoons
The World's Greatest Sex Cartoons

Front cover and title page illustrations by Gren Jones MBE.
Designed by Pinpoint Design.
Edited by Mark Bryant.
Printed and bound in Spain.

Exley Publications Ltd, 16 Chalk Hill, Watford, Herts WD1 4BN, UK.
Exley Giftbooks, 232 Madison Avenue, Suite 1206, NY 10016, USA.

Published simultaneously in 1996 by Exley Publications in Great Britain
and Exley Giftbooks in the USA.

Selection © Exley Publications Ltd 1996.
The copyright for each cartoon remains with the cartoonist.

ISBN 1-85015-800-2

THANK YOU

We would like to thank all the cartoonists who submitted entries for *The World's Greatest RUGBY CARTOONS*. They came in from
many parts of the world – including Israel, New Zealand, Nigeria, Pakistan, Romania, Russia, Spain, and the United Kingdom.

Special thanks go to the cartoonists whose work appears in the final book. They include Femi Adetunji page 45; Les Barton
pages 26, 66; Rog Bowles pages 8, 22, 31, 53, 61; Ray Chesterton pages 7, 16, 23, 27, 33, 55, 64, 68, 72, 74, 77; Costinel
page 43; Pat Drennan page 17; Stidley Easel page 9; Noel Ford pages 11, 35, 52, 78; Xaquin Marin Formoso page 40;
Martin Honeysett page 20; Tony Husband pages 21, 24, 36, 42, 50, 56, 62, 67, 73, 79; Chic Jacob pages 19, 58, 70; Mik
Jago page 12; Gren Jones MBE cover and title page; Ham Khan pages 4, 39, 47; Larry pages 5, 13, 25, 29, 37, 46, 51, 54,
59, 71; Constantin Pavel page 30; Ken Pyne page 38; Viv Quillin page 49; Bryan Reading page 15; Bill Stott pages 10, 18, 32,
44, 65, 69; Alex Talimonov pages 57, 76; Geoff Thompson page 63; Colin Whittock pages 6, 14, 28, 34, 41, 48, 60, 75.

Every effort has been made to trace the copyright holders of cartoons in this book. However, any error will gladly be corrected
by the publisher for future printings.

THE WORLD'S GREATEST
RUGBY
CARTOONS

EDITED BY
Mark Bryant

◧ EXLEY
NEW YORK • WATFORD, UK

"I'll be glad when Charlie gets his new lenses –
that's the fifth ref he's had in six weeks!"

"Where's that miserable apology for a
second-row forward got to now!"

The Detective

"C..C..Can I call you back later?"

"Rugby is <u>not</u> violent. I'll belt the next bloke who says it is!"

"Well at least it was a good clean game!"

13

"We can't drop Grotley – he's the only one
who knows all the verses of 'Eskimo Nell' . . . !"

Reading

*"That's always been Smith's trouble – bags of speed,
but no sense of direction."*

"Just relax – your surgeon is the best front row forward in the business!"

"OK – I've got him . . ."

"It only picks up rugby!"

"He just can't wait until he's old enough
to start playing rugby."

"Do I prefer England to you . . . darling, I prefer Wales to you!"

The Harpist

"Well kicked, Wanderers!"

"Darling, he told his first vulgar rugby joke!"

"My name – David, sir!"

"Couldn't you <u>ask</u> mother to stop talking when you want to hear the results?"

"It was a great try, pity everyone landed on him!"

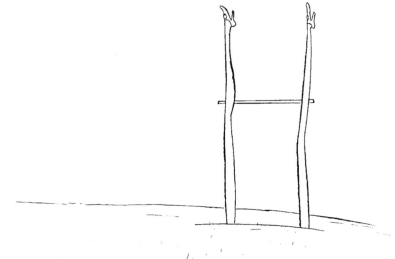

C. PAVEL

The Booking

"And in the fifth team, youth and maturity are united by one common factor – total lack of ability!"

"We've just realized the Padre and I played against each other in the 'Varsity Match ten years ago – I'm going round to his place for a good old natter about it this evening."

"Etiquette – You never, <u>never</u> fart in the scrum!"

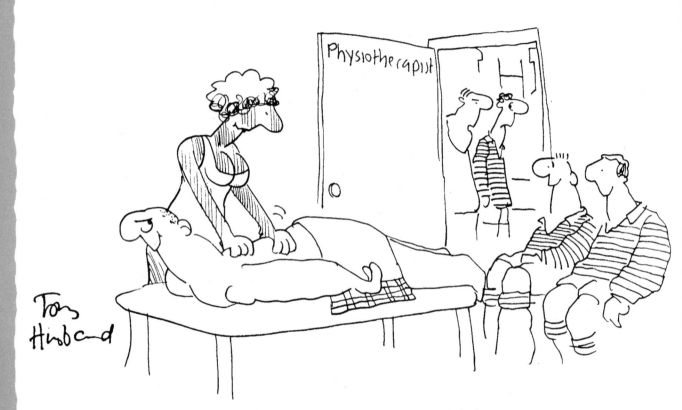

"Tell you what, we've had a lot more injuries since the new physio arrived."

"If you ask me it's all becoming too commercialized."

"Fitness test . . . !"

"He definitely needs his eyes testing."

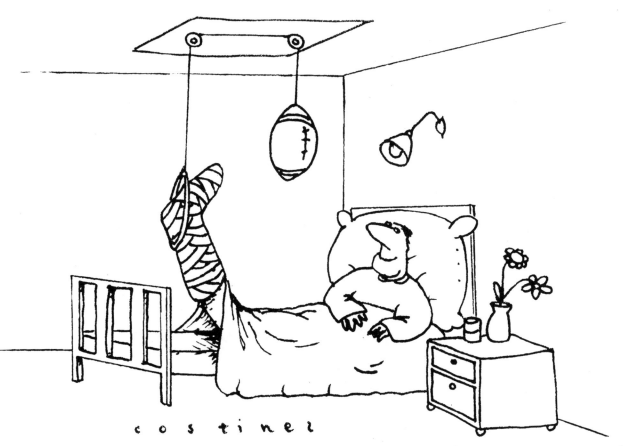

costineł

43

"For heaven's sake – what now?"

The Origin of Rugby!

"Come now, we can't solve our problems by running away!"

"You're going to meet a tall dark scrum-half
and loose a few teeth in the process!"

50

The Cobbler

"You're seeing him at his worst – he's not usually like this!"

"Blimey – we could do with some of those in the back four!"

"My lads say they're not playing against that
until they've heard it speak!"

"I still say your evidence is only circumstantial . . . !"

The Juggler

"How did you know I was a rugby player?"

"Playing for money makes me feel dirty."

"It's your birthday, you say what you'd like to do – watch
Blackheath or go over and see the seven-a-sides."

"OK lightnin' release the ball!"

"It's a jungle out there!"

"That reminds me, what time
does the rugby kick off today?"

"Whatever you do, don't look round!"

"Aaaagh! I'm stamping on my own hand!"

"Ah! It's my ear! I thought you
were sending me off!"

"I'll tell you exactly what happened last night: you came in drunk as a lord, screamed 'Got to find touch, chaps', and kicked my new hat straight through that window!"

"Don't be fooled. It's the match
ball he sticks down there!"

"Are you allowing for this in injury time, ref?"

"Would you mind taking over?
I've had a sudden loss of confidence!"

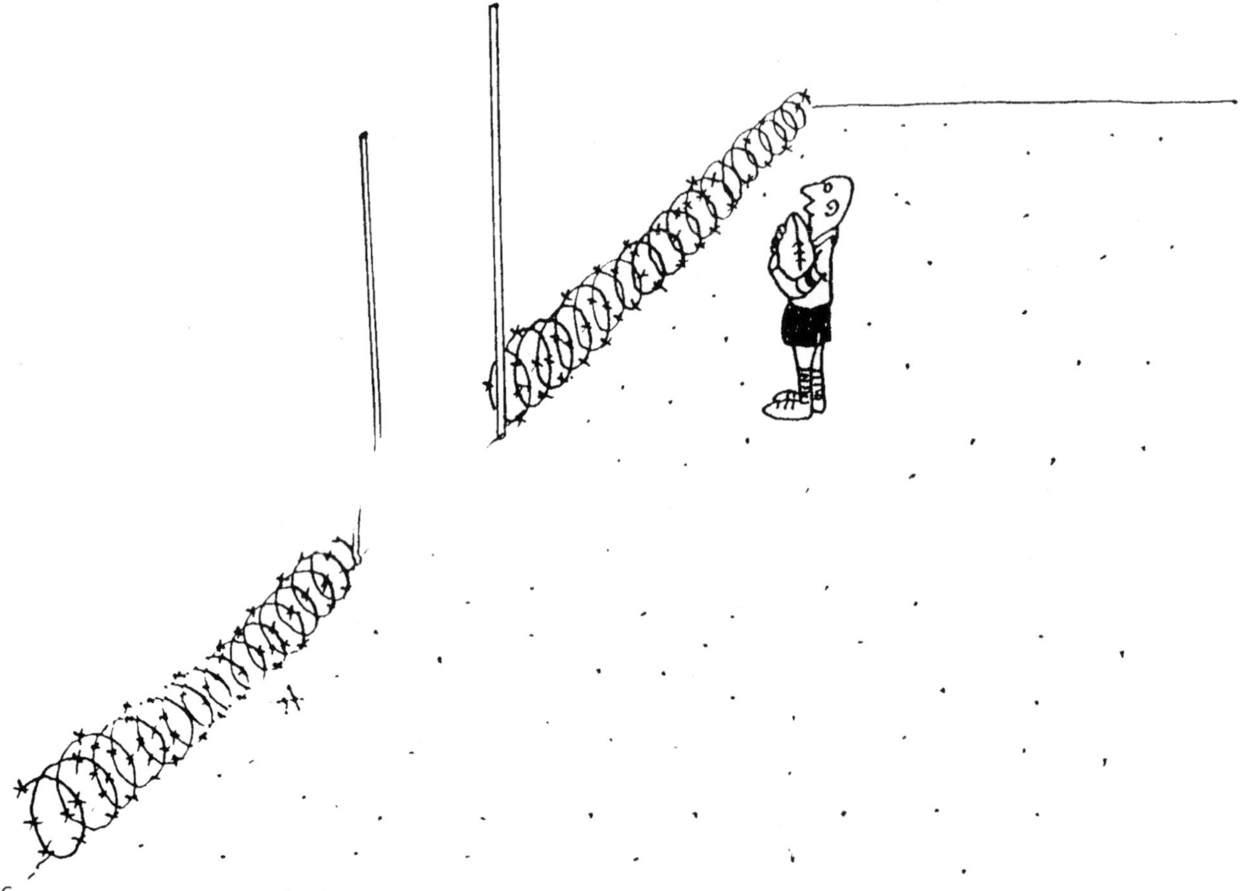

"Low, Johnson – go for him low."

"No, it didn't happen in the _GAME_ – one of the
lads pinched his rubber duck in the bath . . ."

"I told you to stop moaning at him!"

Books in the "World's Greatest" series
($4.99 £2.99 paperback)

The World's Greatest Business Cartoons
The World's Greatest Cat Cartoons
The World's Greatest Computer Cartoons
The World's Greatest Dad Cartoons
The World's Greatest Do-It-Yourself Cartoons
The World's Greatest Golf Cartoons
The World's Greatest Keep-Fit Cartoons
The World's Greatest Marriage Cartoons
The World's Greatest Middle Age Cartoons
The World's Greatest Sex Cartoons

Books in the "Victim's Guide" series
($4.99 £2.99 paperback)

Award winning cartoonist Roland Fiddy sees the funny side to life's phobias, nightmares and catastrophes.

The Victim's Guide to Air Travel
The Victim's Guide to The Baby
The Victim's Guide to The Boss
The Victim's Guide to Christmas
The Victim's Guide to The Dentist
The Victim's Guide to The Doctor
The Victim's Guide to Middle Age

Books in the "Crazy World" series
($4.99 £2.99 paperback)

The Crazy World of Aerobics
The Crazy World of Cats
The Crazy World of Cricket
The Crazy World of Gardening
The Crazy World of Golf
The Crazy World of the Handyman
The Crazy World of Hospitals
The Crazy World of Housework
The Crazy World of Learning to Drive
The Crazy World of Love
The Crazy World of Marriage
The Crazy World of Rugby
The Crazy World of Sailing
The Crazy World of School
The Crazy World of Sex
The Crazy World of Soccer

Books in the "Fanatics" series
($4.99 £2.99 paperback)

The **Fanatic's Guides** are perfect presents for everyone with a hobby that has got out of hand. Eighty pages of hilarious black and white cartoons by Roland Fiddy.

The Fanatic's Guide to The Bed
The Fanatic's Guide to Diets
The Fanatic's Guide to Dogs
The Fanatic's Guide to Money
The Fanatic's Guide to Skiing
The Fanatic's Guide to Sports

The following titles are also available in paperback and in a new smaller full colour hardback format ($6.99 £3.99):

The Fanatic's Guide to Cats
The Fanatic's Guide to Computers
The Fanatic's Guide to Dads
The Fanatic's Guide to D.I.Y.
The Fanatic's Guide to Golf
The Fanatic's Guide to Husbands
The Fanatic's Guide to Love
The Fanatic's Guide to Sex

Great Britain: Order these super books from your local bookseller or from Exley Publications Ltd, 16 Chalk Hill, Watford, Herts WD1 4BN. (Please send £1.30 to cover postage and packing on 1 book, £2.60 on 2 or more books.)